PROPERTIES OF MATTER
Matter & Energy Series

Written by George Graybill, Ph. D.

GRADES 5 - 8
Reading Levels 3 - 4

Classroom Complete Press

P.O. Box 19729
San Diego, CA 92159
Tel: 1-800-663-3609 / Fax: 1-800-663-3608
Email: service@classroomcompletepress.com

www.classroomcompletepress.com

ISBN-13: 978-1-55319-370-8
ISBN-10: 1-55319-370-9
© 2007

Permission to Reproduce

Critical Thinking Skills

Properties of Matter

Skills For Critical Thinking	Reading Comprehension							Hands-on Activities
	Section 1	Section 2	Section 3	Section 4	Section 5	Section 6	Section 7	
LEVEL 1 Knowledge								
• List Details/Facts	✓	✓					✓	
• Recall Information	✓	✓	✓		✓	✓	✓	
• Match Vocab. to Definitions	✓	✓			✓			
• Define Vocabulary			✓	✓	✓	✓		
• Label Diagrams						✓		✓
• Recognize Validity (T/F)	✓	✓	✓	✓	✓	✓	✓	
LEVEL 2 Comprehension								
• Demonstrate Understanding	✓	✓	✓	✓	✓	✓	✓	✓
• Explain Scientific Causation		✓	✓		✓	✓		
• Rephrasing Vocab. Meaning		✓	✓					
• Describe			✓	✓	✓		✓	
• Classify into Scientific Groups	✓		✓	✓			✓	
LEVEL 3 Application								
• Application to Own Life		✓	✓		✓			
• Model Scientific Process	✓				✓	✓		✓
• Organize and Classify Facts	✓		✓		✓	✓	✓	✓
• Utilize Alternative Research Tools								✓
LEVEL 4 Analysis								
• Distinguish Roles/Meanings								
• Make Inferences	✓				✓	✓	✓	✓
• Draw Conclusions Based on Facts Provided	✓			✓		✓	✓	✓
• Classify Based on Facts Researched		✓		✓	✓			
LEVEL 5 Synthesis								
• Compile Research Information		✓		✓	✓			✓
• Design and Application			✓					✓
• Create and Construct			✓		✓	✓		✓
• Imagine Self in Scientific Role								✓
LEVEL 6 Evaluation								
• State and Defend an Opinion				✓	✓	✓		✓
• Justify Choices for Research Topics								
• Defend Selections and Reasoning					✓			✓

Based on Bloom's Taxonomy

Contents

• • • • • • • • • • • • • • • • •

FREE! 6 Bonus Activities!

<u>3 EASY STEPS</u> to receive your 6 Bonus Activities!
- Go to our website:
  www.classroomcompletepress.com\bonus
- Click on item CC4504 – Properties of Matter
- Enter pass code CC4504D

Assessment Rubric

• •

Properties of Matter

Student's Name: _____ Assignment: _____ Level: _____

	Level 1	Level 2	Level 3	Level 4
Understanding Concepts	Demonstrates a limited understanding of concepts. Requires teacher intervention.	Demonstrates a basic understanding of concepts. Requires little teacher intervention.	Demonstrates a good understanding of concepts. Requires no teacher intervention.	Demonstrates a thorough understanding of concepts. Requires no teacher intervention.
Analysis & Application of Key Concepts	Limited application and interpretation in activity responses	Basic application and interpretation in activity responses	Good application and interpretation in activity responses	Strong application and interpretation in activity responses
Creativity and Imagination	Limited creativity and imagination applied in projects and activities	Some creativity and imagination applied in projects and activities	Satisfactory level of creativity and imagination applied in projects and activities	Beyond expected creativity and imagination applied in projects and activities
Application of Own Interests	Limited application of own interests in independent or group environment	Basic application of own interests in independent or group environment	Good application of own interests in independent or group environment	Strong application of own interests in independent or group environment

STRENGTHS:

WEAKNESSES:

NEXT STEPS:

Teacher Guide

Our resource has been created for ease of use by both TEACHERS and STUDENTS alike.

Introduction

This resource provides ready-to-use information and activities for remedial students in grades five to eight. Written to grade and using simplified language and vocabulary, **science** concepts are presented in a way that makes them more accessible to students and easier to understand. Comprised of reading passages, student activities and mini posters, our resource can be used effectively for whole-class, small group and independent work.

How Is Our Resource Organized?

STUDENT HANDOUTS

Reading passages and **activities** (in the form of reproducible worksheets) make up the majority of our resource. The reading passages present important grade-appropriate information and concepts related to the topic. Embedded in each passage are one or more questions that ensure students understand what they have read.

For each reading passage there are BEFORE YOU READ activities and AFTER YOU READ activities.

- The BEFORE YOU READ activities prepare students for reading by setting a purpose for reading. They stimulate background knowledge and experience, and guide students to make connections between what they know and what they will learn. Important concepts and vocabulary are also presented.

- The AFTER YOU READ activities check students' comprehension of the concepts presented in the reading passage and extend their learning. Students are asked to give thoughtful consideration of the reading passage through creative and evaluative short-answer questions, research, and extension activities.

Hands-on activities are included to further develop students' thinking skills and understanding of the concepts. The **Assessment Rubric** (*page 4*) is a useful tool for evaluating students' responses to many of the activities in our resource. The **Comprehension Quiz** (*page 48*) can be used for either a follow-up review or assessment at the completion of the unit.

PICTURE CUES

This resource contains three main types of pages, each with a different purpose and use. A **Picture Cue** at the top of each page shows, at a glance, what the page is for.

Teacher Guide
- Information and tools for the teacher

Student Handout
- Reproducible worksheets and activities

Easy Marking™ Answer Key
- Answers for student activities

EASY MARKING™ ANSWER KEY

Marking students' worksheets is fast and easy with this **Answer Key**. Answers are listed in columns – just line up the column with its corresponding worksheet, as shown, and see how every question matches up with its answer!

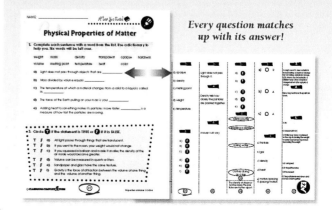

Every question matches up with its answer!

Bloom's Taxonomy

Our resource is an effective tool for any SCIENCE PROGRAM.

Bloom's Taxonomy* for Reading Comprehension

The activities in our resource engage and build the full range of thinking skills that are essential for students' reading comprehension and understanding of important science concepts. Based on the six levels of thinking in Bloom's Taxonomy, and using language at a remedial level, information and questions are given that challenge students to not only recall what they have read, but move beyond this to understand the text and concepts through higher-order thinking. By using higher-order skills of application, analysis, synthesis and evaluation, students become active readers, drawing more meaning from the text, attaining a greater understanding of concepts, and applying and extending their learning in more sophisticated ways.

Our resource, therefore, is an effective tool for any Science program. Whether it is used in whole or in part, or adapted to meet individual student needs, our resource provides teachers with essential information and questions to ask, inspiring students' interest, creativity, and promoting meaningful learning.

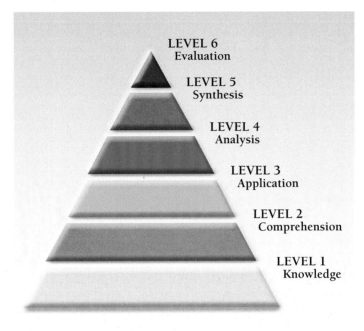

LEVEL 6 Evaluation
LEVEL 5 Synthesis
LEVEL 4 Analysis
LEVEL 3 Application
LEVEL 2 Comprehension
LEVEL 1 Knowledge

BLOOM'S TAXONOMY:
6 LEVELS OF THINKING

*Bloom's Taxonomy is a widely used tool by educators for classifying learning objectives, and is based on the work of Benjamin Bloom.

Vocabulary

atom	evaporate	mass	physical change	solid
boil	flammable	matter	physical property	solubility
chemical change	force	melt	property	solution
chemical property	freeze	metal oxide	pure material	texture
color	gas	mixture	rot resistant	translucent
condensation	gravity	molecule	rust resistant	transparent
density	hardness	opaque	shape	volume
dissolve	liquid	particle	smell	weight

NAME: _____

What is Matter?

1. Complete each sentence with a word from the list. Use a dictionary to help you.

atom   mass   matter   molecule   particle

a) _____s are made up of more than one atom.

b) The scientific word that is closest to the everyday word "stuff" is _____.

c) _Atom_____s cannot be divided into smaller bits with everyday tools.

d) Atoms and molecules are very small _Particl___s.

e) _mass_____ is the property of an object that tells how much matter it contains.

2. The picture below shows sunlight shining on a balloon. Circle (Yes) or (No) to the following questions.

(Yes)	**No**	**a)** Is the balloon made of matter?
(Yes)	**No**	**b)** Is there any matter inside the balloon?
Yes	**(No)**	**c)** Is the sunlight made of matter?
(Yes)	**No**	**d)** Is there matter in the air that surrounds the balloon?
(Yes)	**No**	**e)** Does the balloon have mass?

What is Matter?

Matter is what people often call "stuff." In fact, "stuff" sounds almost like the German word for matter, "Stoff." All objects and materials we can touch are made of matter, and all matter takes up space. Rocks, trees, bugs, water, and air are all forms of matter. *You* are matter. Light, sound, heat, ideas, and wishes are *not* matter.

Different objects have different amounts of matter. When we measure the amount of matter in something, we say we measure the **property** called **mass**. As long as nothing is added to or removed from an object, its mass does not change. Later, we will look at other properties of matter like **density** and **weight**.

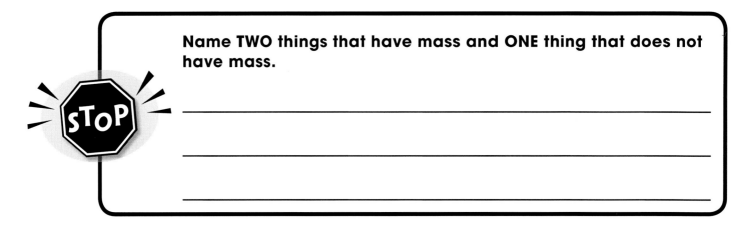

Name TWO things that have mass and ONE thing that does not have mass.

_____

_____

_____

People have always wanted to know the true nature of matter. For thousands of years most people thought that matter could be divided into smaller and smaller pieces forever. When scientists had better tools, they found that matter is really made of tiny bits. These bits, called **atoms**, cannot be divided into smaller parts with everyday tools. Atoms are one kind of **particle**. When atoms stick together in a group, they form another type of particle called a **molecule**. All the particles in a pure material are the same.

Atoms are very, very small. They are so small that *billions* of them make up a speck of dust. If you had one penny for every atom *in* a penny, you would have much more money than everyone in the world put together!

After You Read

What is Matter?

1. Put a check mark (✓) next to the answer that is most correct.

a) It is possible to measure the mass of all of these things, *except*

- ○ **A** a fly
- ◉ **(B)** a sunbeam
- ○ **C** a polar bear
- ○ **D** a cotton ball

b) Which of these is a property?

- ○ **A** atom
- ◉ **(B)** mass
- ○ **C** molecule
- ○ **D** particle

c) Which of these pairs of words *both* refer to kinds of particles?

- ○ **A** matter and mass
- ○ **B** mass and atom
- ◉ **C** atom and ~~molecule~~ ✓
- ○ **D** molecule and matter

2. a) ~~Cross out~~ the words for things that have no mass.

air   ~~sound~~   the planet Earth   a deep ~~thought~~   an ant   an elephant

b) (Circle) the words for things that have the property of mass.

(air)   sound   (the planet Earth)   a deep thought   (an ant)   (an elephant)

c) <u>Underline</u> the words for things made of matter.

<u>air</u>   sound   the planet Earth   a deep thought   <u>an ant</u>   <u>an elephant</u>

NAME: _____

What Is Matter?

3. Imagine trying to divide a piece of gold into smaller and smaller pieces. Even if you could see and cut the smallest pieces of gold, you would reach a point where you would have to stop. Explain why you would have to stop dividing the gold.

_____

_____

4. A cookie has a certain mass. Explain why breaking the cookie in half does not change its mass.

_____

_____

Extensions & Applications

5. People have been trying to understand the true nature of matter for a long time. People in ancient Greece thought about matter more than 2000 years ago. The big question was whether matter is made of the small bits we call atoms or whether it is just some sort of uniform stuff that can be divided again and again without end. If matter can be divided forever, we would say it is **continuous.** So is matter separate bits, or is it continuous?

a) Study the history of this question by learning what a few famous thinkers and scientists had to say about it.

FIRST, find out what two ancient Greeks, named **Democritus** and **Aristotle** thought. Also try to find out which one most people believed.

NEXT, learn what **John Dalton** said about matter and atoms 200 years ago. Did other scientists believe him?

Show what you found out about the history of ideas about matter by writing names in the table on the next page.

b) We know now that matter is made of separate bits called atoms. Suppose you didn't know this. Which would make more sense: that things are made of separate bits or that things are continuous? Tell why you think this.

_____

_____

What Is Matter?

IDEAS ABOUT MATTER

Question	Name of the person or persons that answers the question
A. Who thought matter is made of particles?	
B. Who thought matter is continuous?	
C. Who did most people believe in ancient times?	
D. Who used experiments and scientific tools to study matter?	
E. Whose ideas about matter were most like what scientists think today?	

Democritus   **John Dalton**   **Aristotle**

NAME: _____

Three States of Matter

1. Materials can be solids, liquids, or gases. Write <u>S</u> after each material that is a solid. Write <u>L</u> after each material that is a liquid. Write <u>G</u> after each material that is a gas.

a) water _____

b) air _____

c) sand _____

d) cooking oil _____

e) candle wax _____

f) steam _____

g) ice _____

2. Fill in each blank with a word from the list.

solid	liquid	gas

a) When something **melts,** it goes from a _____ to a _____.

b) When something **boils,** it goes from a _____ to a _____.

c) When something **freezes,** it goes from a _____ to a _____.

NAME: _____

Three States of Matter

You may know that most materials can take three different forms called **solid, liquid,** and **gas.** These forms are known as the three **states of matter.** We are most familiar with the three states of water. Solid water is ice; we drink liquid water; and water as a gas is called steam or water vapor. Some people think fog and clouds are gas, but they are actually very small drops of liquid water.

Each state of matter has its own **properties:**

Solids have a fixed **shape** and a fixed **volume.** This means that a solid's shape and volume always stay the same.

Liquids do not have a fixed shape; they take the shape of their container. Liquids do have a fixed volume.

Gases take the shape of their container, *and* they completely fill their container. So gases do not have a fixed shape or a fixed volume.

Show the properties of the three states of matter by writing YES or NO in each box of the table below.

State of Matter	Does it have a fixed shape?	Does it have a fixed volume?
Solid		
Liquid		
Gas		

But why *are* there different states of matter? What makes a material change from one state to another? We can answer these questions by looking at the behavior of the **particles** in each state. Remember that all matter is made up of very small particles called atoms and molecules.

Three States of Matter

Particles are *always* moving, but they move differently in different states. In solids, particles move back and forth in the same spot. They cannot change positions or move from one place to another. Because the particles cannot change positions, solids cannot change their shape.

In liquids, particles move more freely and are able to change positions with each other. Because particles can change position, liquids can change shape. In both solids and liquids, particles are kept close together by the **forces** between them. These forces pull the particles together, keeping the volume small.

The particles of gases move fastest and most freely. Gas particles are far apart and so do not pull on each other very much. Because gas particles move so freely, they can race off to fill every part of their container. When a liquid becomes a gas, it fills about a thousand times more space.

We can understand why materials change state by thinking about how particles move. When we add heat to a material, its particles begin to move faster. As particles speed up, the temperature of the material rises. In other words, temperature measures particle speed. When the particles in a solid reach a certain speed, they break free of their fixed positions. This is when something **melts.** The temperature at which particles move fast enough to melt is called the **melting point.** The melting point of water is 32°F.

When the particles in a liquid move fast enough to break away from the pull they have on each other, they go into the gas state. If the particles break free slowly, one at a time, this is called **evaporation.** If particles break free suddenly, in large groups, this is called **boiling.** The temperature that moves particles fast enough to boil is called the **boiling point.** The boiling point of water is 212°F.

Removing heat can change a gas to a liquid (**condensation**) and can change a liquid to a solid (**freezing**).

NAME: _____

Three States of Matter

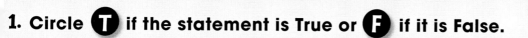

1. Circle T if the statement is True or F if it is False.

T (F) **a)** Particles in a solid cannot move.

(T) F **b)** Particles in a gas are much farther apart than particles in a liquid.

T (F) **c)** Liquids have fixed shape that cannot change.

T (F) **d)** Materials lose mass when they go from liquid to gas.

(T) F **e)** When particles of a material move faster, the temperature of the material goes up.

2. Use the words in the list to answer each question. Two words will be used more than once.

boiling   condensing   evaporating

freezing   melting

mistake

__Freesing__ **a)** Which is a change from liquid to solid?

__condensation__ **b)** Which is a change from gas to liquid?

__melting__ **c)** Which can happen when heat is added to a solid?

__boiling or emperation__ **d)** Which **two** things can happen when heat is added to a liquid?

__boiling__ **e)** What happens when particles break free from their fixed positions?

__frelsing?__ **f)** What change is happening when clouds form in the sky, dew forms on grass, or water droplets form on a bathroom mirror?

NAME: _____

Three States of Matter

3. Why can't solid things change their shape? Use the word "particles" in your explanation.

_____

_____

4. The temperature of a bowl of hot soup goes down after the soup is poured into a bowl. What is happening to the <u>motion</u> of the particles in the soup as it cools?

_____

_____

5. Gases have very low densities. What does this show about the <u>distance</u> between gas particles?

_____

_____

Extensions & Applications

6. a) Use the graphic organizer on the next page to organize what you have learned about states of matter. The arrows show the **direction of change** from one state to another. Write the name of each change. Tell whether the change is caused by adding heat or removing heat. Tell whether the change makes the particles move faster or slower. Some of the answers have been done for you.

b) We can understand how particles move in the three states by thinking of something we can see that moves the same way. For example, particles in a solid move like people riding in a bus on a bumpy road.

The people in the bus are always in motion because the bus is in motion. Yet, they never change position because they don't change seats. The speed of the bus is like temperature. The greater the bus speed, the faster the people bounce around.

Now do the same for the other two states of matter.

Think of a type of motion you can see that is like the **motion of particles in a liquid.** You may write a complete description of the motion, or draw a detailed picture of the motion.

Think of a type of motion you can see that is like the **motion of particles in a gas.** You may write a complete description of the motion, or draw a detailed picture of the motion.

Three States of Matter

The Gas State

A. Name of change:
_____

B. Heat added or removed?
_____

C. Particles move faster or slower?
_____

J. Name of change: <u>boiling or evaporation</u>

K. Heat added or removed?
_____

L. Particles move faster or slower?
_____

The Liquid State

D. Name of change:
_____

E. Heat added or removed? <u>removed</u>

F. Particles move faster or slower?
_____

G. Name of change:
_____

H. Heat added or removed?
_____

I. Particles move faster or slower? <u>faster</u>

The Solid State

Physical Properties of Matter

Before You Read

1. Put a check mark (✓) next to the answer that is most correct.

a) What do we use to describe a material?

○ **A** its name
○ **B** its properties
○ **C** who discovered it
○ **D** where it came from

b) What do we measure to find out how much matter is in something?

○ **A** height
○ **B** length
○ **C** mass
○ **D** temperature

c) What keeps us from floating off into space?

○ **A** gravity
○ **B** friction
○ **C** air pressure
○ **D** Earth's rotation

2. Draw one line from each word on the left to the meaning of the word on the right.

density	a)	How rough or smooth the surface of something is
mass	b)	Something you can see through
texture	c)	How much matter is in something
transparent	d)	How much space something takes up
volume	e)	How tightly particles are packed in a material

NAME: _____

Physical Properties of Matter

We describe materials by their **properties.** Some pl properties tell us how much material is present.

Volume tells us how much space a material takes up. In some countries volume is measured in pints, quarts, and gallons. In other countries volume is measured in liters and milliliters. For example, a quart of milk has a little less volume than a liter of milk.

You learned earlier that mass is a measure of how much matter is in something. Mass is measured in grams or kilograms. In some countries, mass is measured in pounds ounces. The mass in every object pulls on the mass in every other object with a force called **gravity**. The more mass the objects have, the harder they pull on each other.

The planet Earth has a lot of mass. The force of Earth's gravity pulls down hard on all the things on its surface. Gravity keeps them from floating off into space. The strength of Earth's pull on something is the thing's **weight**. The more mass an object has, the harder Earth pulls on it, and the more weight it has.

The moon has less mass than Earth. If you went to the moon, you would have **less** weight because the moon would not pull as hard on your mass. Your mass on the moon would be **the same** because you would still have the same amount of matter in your body.

When you jump into the air, you are always pulled back to the Earth by GRAVITY. You can feel the pull of gravity between yourself and the Earth. Explain why you CANNOT feel the pull of gravity between yourself and another person.

_____

_____

Physical Properties of Matter

Density is another property of matter. Density tells how tightly the particles of matter are packed together. To find the density of something, **divide its mass by its volume.** One gram of water has a volume of one milliliter. One divided by one equals one, so water has a density of one gram per milliliter. Mass is also measured in pounds, and volume is also measured in cubic feet. Measuring this way, the density of water is 62 pounds per cubic foot. Density does not change with amount. One gram of water has the same density as 100 grams of water.

Earlier we learned about boiling point, melting point, and temperature. These are also physical properties of matter. Some other common properties you may know about are shape, color, smell, hardness, and **texture**. Texture tells how rough or smooth the surface of an object is.

Other physical properties have to do with light. If light passes through an object, we say it is **transparent**. Glass and water are transparent. If no light passes through something, we say it is **opaque**. You are opaque. If some, but not all, light passes through something, it is **translucent**. Tissue paper and milk are translucent.

If you want to find out what a material is, some properties can be helpful. Finding the density, boiling point, melting point, color, smell, hardness, and transparency are most helpful. Knowing the temperature, mass, weight, and volume are no help at all.

NAME: _____

Physical Properties of Matter

1. Complete each sentence with a word from the list. Use a dictionary to help you. Six words will be left over.

weight   mass   density   transparent   opaque   hardness

volume   melting point   temperature   heat   color

a) Light does not pass through objects that are _____.

b) Mass divided by volume equals _____.

c) The temperature at which a material changes from a solid to a liquid is called its _____.

d) The force of the Earth pulling on your mass is your _____.

e) Adding heat to something makes its particles move faster. _____ is a measure of how fast the particles are moving.

2. Circle T if the statement is TRUE or F if it is FALSE.

T F **a)** All light passes through things that are translucent.

T F **b)** If you went to the moon, your weight would not change.

T F **c)** If you squeezed a balloon and made it smaller, the density of the air inside would become greater.

T F **d)** Volume can be measured in quarts or liters.

T F **e)** Sandpaper and glass have the same texture.

T F **f)** Gravity is the force of attraction between the volume of one thing and the volume of another thing.

Physical Properties of Matter

3. What does the word **opaque** mean?

_____

_____

4. Explain what the density of an object tells us about the particles the object is made of.

_____

_____

Extensions & Applications

5. Measure or describe as many PROPERTIES as you can for an egg and for a glass of water.

Part A

For the egg, describe the properties color, texture, hardness, and shape. Also tell whether the egg is transparent, translucent, opaque. Tell whether the water is transparent, translucent, opaque.

Part B

For the next part, you will need a thermometer, a measuring cup, a kitchen stove or hot plate, and a scale or balance. If you cannot get these tools, describe how you would use them.

Measure the **temperature** of the water. Measure the **boiling point** of the water or tell how you would measure it.

Use the measuring cup to measure the volume of the water. Use the measuring cup *and* the water to measure the volume of the egg.

Use the balance to measure the mass of the egg. How would you measure the mass of the water?

What is the density of the water? What is the density of the egg?

NAME: _____

Physical Changes of Matter

1. Circle **T** if the statement is **TRUE** or **F** if it is **FALSE**.

T   F   **a)**   During a physical change a new kind of matter is formed.

T   F   **b)**   After a material has a physical change it is made of different kind of particles.

T   F   **c)**   Melting is a physical change.

T   F   **d)**   Adding heat to a material can cause a physical change.

T   F   **e)**   When a liquid freezes, its particles get harder.

2. Circle the changes that are physical changes.

Melting butter

Breaking a pretzel

Digesting food

Boiling water

A nail rusting

Burning a match

Clothes drying on a line

Physical Changes of Matter

Things can change in two ways: **physical changes** and **chemical changes**. A physical change makes something look different, but it is still the same material made of the same kinds of particles. A chemical change causes a whole new material to form. The new material is different because the particles are different. We will soon learn more about chemical changes. First we will look at physical changes.

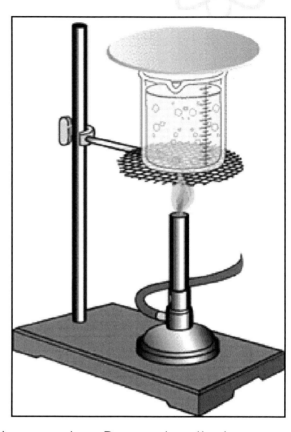

We have studied how materials can change from solid to liquid to gas and back again. These are all physical changes because no new material is formed. Ice, liquid water, and steam are all made of water particles. Suppose an ice cube is melted, and then the melted water is all boiled away. Now all the water is water vapor. We could condense the water vapor back to liquid water and then freeze that water. The ice we get will be just the same as the ice we started with.

Adding heat causes materials to melt and boil. Adding or removing heat can cause other physical changes, too. Remember that heat makes particles move faster. Heat also makes particles move farther apart. When particles move farther apart the material takes up more space. A material that takes up more space has a bigger volume. You can see this happen to a balloon. If you take a balloon out of the refrigerator and place it in warm sunlight, it will get larger. When volume gets larger, density gets smaller because the particles are not as close together.

Is the density of steam MORE or LESS than the density of water? Explain your answer using the word "particles".

STOP

_____

_____

_____

Physical Changes of Matter

Heat can also change the color of things. Iron changes from black to red when it gets very hot. When it cools, the color goes back to black. Heat can change the property of hardness too. Think what happens to butter or a wax candle when you add heat.

Changing shape and breaking are physical changes that you see every day. All of these are physical changes:

- stretching a rubber band

- smashing a pumpkin

- sitting on a pillow

- breaking a window

- slicing a carrot

- squashing a rotten tomato

All of these changes make something look very different. None of these changes make a new kind of material.

It is important to understand that the particles *themselves* do not change in a physical change. When water freezes, the water molecules do not become hard. When water boils, it takes up more space, but not because the molecules swell up. Particles of a material are the same size and shape in a solid, liquid, or gas. It is the *movement* and space between particles that cause the three states to be different.

Later we will learn about a physical change called **dissolving**. This is what happens when we add salt to water.

Physical Changes of Matter

1. Put a check mark (✓) next to the answer that is most correct.

a) What happens when particles of a material move farther apart?

○ **A** A new material is formed.
○ **B** The particles become larger.
○ **C** The material becomes more dense.
○ **D** The volume of the material becomes greater.

b) A physical change can do all of these things, *except*

○ **A** form a new material.
○ **B** make something smaller.
○ **C** change a liquid into a gas.
○ **D** change the color of something.

c) What happens to particles of a material when heat is added?

○ **A** The particles move faster.
○ **B** The particles are destroyed.
○ **C** The particles become softer.
○ **D** The particles move closer together.

2. Fill in each blank with a word from the list. Four words will be left over.

gas	solid	liquid	motion	heat
volume	density	freezing	particle	spacing

Water and ice are made of the same kind of _____s.
a

Particles in a _____ are much farther apart than the particles in a liquid.
b

When volume gets larger, _____ gets smaller.
c

Adding _____ to a material makes its particles move faster.
d

The state a material is in depends on the _____ and _____
e   **f**

of the particles of the material.

Physical Changes of Matter

3. How is a physical change different from a chemical change?

_____

_____

4. How does removing heat from a material change the motion of its particles?

_____

_____

Extensions & Applications

5. Physical Changes Caused By Heat

a) This experiment shows that matter does not change during a physical change.

Weigh a cup of water. Put the water in a refrigerator freezer until it is frozen. Remove the frozen water and weigh it again. Let it melt and weigh it one more time.

    A. Are the particles of melted water any different than they were before the experiment?

    B. Are the weights the same?

    C. If the weights are different, use the words "evaporation" and "condensation" to explain the differences.

b) Find an empty plastic soda or water bottle. Put the cap on loosely and run hot water over the bottle for a few minutes. Quickly screw the cap tight and put the bottle in the refrigerator freezer.

Wait 30 minutes and look at the bottle.

    A. What happened to the volume of air in the bottle?

    B. What happened to the mass of air in the bottle?

    C. What happened to the density of the air in the bottle?

    D. How did the motion and spacing of the air particles in the bottle change?

Physical Changes vs. Chemical Changes

1. **Some changes are described below. Write P beside the changes that are physical changes. Write C beside the changes that are chemical changes.**

_____ **a)** Water boils on a stove.

_____ **b)** An old penny, lost in the grass, turns green.

_____ **c)** Fireworks explode in the night sky.

_____ **d)** Frost forms on a pumpkin.

_____ **e)** An old Jack-O-lantern begins to rot.

2. **Circle T if the statement is TRUE or F if it is FALSE.**

T F **a)** Chemical changes happen only in things that are alive.

T F **b)** Physical changes happen only in things that are not alive.

T F **c)** The way atoms are fastened together changes during a chemical change.

T F **d)** Atoms and molecules are both particles.

T F **e)** If a material changes color, it is proof that a chemical change is happening.

Physical Changes vs. Chemical Changes

We learned that **chemical changes** cause new materials to be formed. What do we mean by *new*? Earlier, we read that particles, called **atoms**, sometimes fasten together to form larger particles, called **molecules**. Sometimes atoms get **rearranged** and fastened in a new way to form different molecules. This is a chemical change. In a physical change, the particles are the same before and after the change.

When clouds begin to form in a clear, blue sky, it looks like a new material is being formed. This is not true. The air is full of many water molecules that we cannot see. They are the gas called water vapor. When they come together to form tiny drops, a cloud appears. This is a physical change because the water molecules did not change. They just went from the gas state to the liquid state.

When hydrogen gas burns, it **combines** with oxygen gas to form water. This is a chemical change because a new material is formed. Atoms in hydrogen and oxygen molecules come apart. Then they fasten together in a new way and form water molecules.

Another example of a chemical change is rust forming on an iron nail. First, oxygen molecules come apart. Then the oxygen atoms fasten onto iron atoms and form a new material. The new material is rust. Rust has the chemical name, iron oxide.

These two examples are both chemical changes because atoms have been rearranged to form new molecules.

Physical Changes vs. Chemical Changes

Do you think it is possible to tell whether a change is chemical or physical by just watching it? It is often hard to tell, but there are some good clues. Flames show a chemical change is taking place. Other signs are not a sure bet. If the change only goes in one **direction**, it is *usually* a chemical change. For example, you can re-freeze a melted ice cube. (This is a physical change.) You cannot un-burn a match. (This is a chemical change).

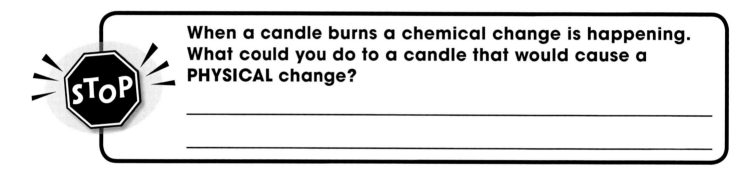

When a candle burns a chemical change is happening. What could you do to a candle that would cause a PHYSICAL change?

_____

_____

When bubbles rise out of a liquid, it may show that a chemical change is forming a gas. But boiling also makes bubbles rise out of a liquid, and that is a physical change. **Explosions** are often chemical changes. Exploding fireworks are a chemical change, but an exploding balloon is a physical change. Changes in color, temperature, and smell can all happen with either a chemical or physical change.

So it may take more than a close look to tell whether a change is chemical or physical. You may need to know more about the materials before and after the change.

Finally, it is good to know that many changes are *both* chemical and physical. A physical change can be only a physical change. Chemical changes usually cause physical changes to happen close by. As you watch a fire in a fireplace, you are seeing a chemical change. But the fire is warming the air, and that is a physical change.

NAME: _____

Physical Changes vs. Chemical Changes

1. Put a check mark (✓) next to the answer that is most correct.

a) **Which is the best sign that a chemical change is happening?**
- ○ **A** bubbles
- ○ **B** flames
- ○ **C** heat
- ○ **D** sound

b) **How many of these changes are chemical changes?**

      clouds forming

      a tomato rotting

      plants making food

- ○ **A** none
- ○ **B** one
- ○ **C** two
- ○ **D** three

c) **What kind of change or changes are happening when water goes over a waterfall?**
- ○ **A** neither a chemical change nor a physical change
- ○ **B** a physical change only
- ○ **C** a chemical change only
- ○ **D** both a physical change and a chemical change

2. Write a word in each blank to complete the sentences.

a) Flames show a _____ change is taking place.

b) Hydrogen and Oxygen react to form _____.

c) Chemical changes always change the way _____ are stuck together in molecules.

d) Adding heat causes a material to change. If removing heat causes the material to return to the way is was, the change was probably a _____ change.

Physical Changes vs. Chemical Changes

3. Use the words "atoms" and "molecules" to explain what happens when a new material is formed during a chemical change.

_____

_____

4. Describe a change you could see that could be *either* a chemical change or a physical change.

_____

_____

Extensions and Applications

5. Change In the Kitchen

Look around a kitchen for ways that materials could change or be made to change using the tools and appliances you see.

List **three physical changes** that could happen in the kitchen. Explain why they are physical changes and not chemical changes. For each change tell whether the material that changes could be returned to the way it was.

List **three chemical changes** that could happen in the kitchen. Explain why they are chemical changes and not physical changes. For each change tell what new material was formed. For each change tell whether the material that changes could be returned to the way it was.

NAME: _____

Chemical Changes and Chemical Properties

1. Circle T if the statement is TRUE or F if it is FALSE.

T   F   **a)**   "Chemical reaction" means the same as "chemical change."

T   F   **b)**   Plants use chemical changes to make food.

T   F   **c)**   Only physical changes happen inside our bodies.

T   F   **d)**   Water combines with hydrogen to make oxygen.

T   F   **e)**   Chemical changes tell how and when a material can change into a new material.

2. Put a check mark (✓) next to the answer that is most correct.

a) Which chemical change happens most slowly?
- ○ **A** a nail rusting
- ○ **B** bread baking
- ○ **C** an egg cooking
- ○ **D** a candle burning

b) What gas do we breathe in that helps our bodies get energy from food?
- ○ **A** hydrogen
- ○ **B** oxygen
- ○ **C** water vapor
- ○ **D** carbon dioxide

c) Which is a chemical property?
- ○ **A** freezes at 32°F (0°C)
- ○ **B** can be stretched
- ○ **C** dissolves in water
- ○ **D** able to burn

Chemical Changes and Chemical Properties

Did you know that chemical changes are taking place all around you all the time? There are also millions of chemical changes happening *inside* you right now. Chemical changes are also called **chemical reactions.**

You have seen many chemical changes that happen when oxygen in the air **combines** with other materials. Oxygen combines slowly with some metals to form **metal oxides**. Oxygen and iron form the oxide we call rust. Have you ever noticed that old pennies are not as shiny as new ones? This is because copper in the penny has reacted with oxygen and other gases. Together they form an outside layer of new materials on the penny.

The chemical reaction we see with pennies is **slow**. What about **fast** oxygen reactions? Anything that burns is reacting quickly with oxygen. This includes wood, wax candles, coal, charcoal, oil, gasoline, and gas used for cooking and heating. The gas carbon dioxide is a new material formed by burning. Water vapor is also formed in most burning reactions. Some materials can react with oxygen very, *very* fast. Then we have an explosion!

We breathe in oxygen which goes all through our body to react with food molecules. This reaction gives us energy. It also forms water and carbon dioxide which we breathe out. Many other chemical changes are taking place all the time in every cell of your body. Some of these changes are: how you grow, how you get sick and then get well, and how you get rid of waste materials.

Chemical Changes and Chemical Properties

Many chemical changes happen in plants, too. The most important one for humans is when plants change carbon dioxide and water into food molecules and oxygen. We need the food to eat and the oxygen to breathe.

Name one way in which oxygen from the air reacts SLOWLY with another material. Name one way in which oxygen reacts QUICKLY with another material. Name one way in which oxygen reacts EXPLOSIVELY with another material.

_____

_____

Here is even another kind of chemical change: new materials are formed when large molecules break into smaller ones. Rotting is this kind of chemical change. For example, when dead leaves rot, molecules break apart into smaller molecules. Some of these molecules then go down into the soil and up through the roots to help make new leaves.

All of these kinds of chemical changes that can happen to a material are called the material's **chemical properties**. If a material can burn, it is **flammable**. If a material will not rust or rot, it is **rust resistant** or **rot resistant**. Materials that do not react at all chemically are called **inert**.

These are the four important things we have been reading about:

1. **Physical properties** tell how a material looks and acts as long it does not change into a new material.

2. **Physical changes** are the ways a material can change into a new form but still be the same material. Physical changes do _not_ change the way atoms are stuck together in molecules.

3. **Chemical properties** tell how and when a material can change into a new material.

4. **Chemical changes** cause a new material to be formed. In chemical changes atoms _always_ change the way they are stuck together to form molecules.

Chemical Changes and Chemical Properties

1. **Circle** the names of things that can react <u>quickly</u> with oxygen.
   <u>Underline</u> the things that react <u>slowly</u> with oxygen.
   Be careful—some of the materials do not react with oxygen at all.

   a glass bottle   a copper penny

   dry firewood   coal

   salt water   gasoline

   an iron nail

2. The materials on the left are the materials <u>before</u> a chemical change. The materials on the right are materials <u>after</u> a chemical change. <u>Draw an arrow</u> from each material on the left to the one n the right that shows the before and after parts of each change.

carbon dioxide and water	carbon dioxide, only	**A**
hydrogen and oxygen	food molecules and oxygen	**B**
oxygen and iron	aluminum oxide	**C**
charcoal and oxygen	water and carbon dioxide	**D**
aluminum and oxygen	water, only	**E**
food molecules and oxygen	rust	**F**

After You Read 📖

• • • • • • • • • • • • • • • • • •

Chemical Changes and Chemical Properties

3. What is the meaning of "chemical change?"

_____

_____

4. What is the meaning of "chemical property?"

_____

_____

Extensions & Applications

5. A Chemical Change

Baking soda and vinegar are things people use in cooking. The chemical name of baking soda is sodium hydrogen carbonate. Vinegar is a mixture of water and acetic acid.

For this experiment, you will need:

baking soda vinegar a balloon a bottle with a small top

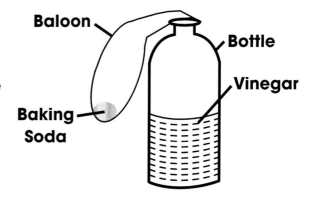

Steps:

1. Add a half inch of water to the bottle. Add a half inch of vinegar to the bottle. Add one tablespoon of baking soda to the balloon.

2. Stretch the balloon over the top of the bottle as shown below. Do not let any baking soda fall into the bottle while you are putting on the balloon.

3. Tip the balloon up so that the baking soda falls into the bottle. Watch the chemical change. New materials formed are liquid water, the gas carbon dioxide, and sodium acetate. Sodium acetate is a solid that dissolves in water. **Where are each of the new materials that formed?**

4. Remember that things need oxygen to burn. Remove the balloon and carefully put a burning match or birthday candle into the neck of the bottle. **Explain what happened to the match.**

Mixtures and Solutions

1. Write each word or group of words beside its meaning.

mixture   solution   dissolve
pure material   physical change   physical property

_____ **a)** a property that tells how a material looks or behaves as long as it does not change into an new material

_____ **b)** a material that is made of only one kind of particle

_____ **c)** what something does when it forms a solution

_____ **d)** a mixture of a material and a liquid where the particles of the materials are completely scattered among each other

_____ **e)** a combination of two pure materials

_____ **f)** a change that does not produce a new materia

2. Circle T if the statement is True or F if it is False.

T F **a)** Air is a mixture.

T F **b)** Ocean water is a mixture.

T F **c)** Sugar is a mixture.

T F **d)** Mixtures can be separated into their parts.

T F **e)** Sand dissolves in water.

NAME: _____

Mixtures and Solutions

Pure materials are made of only one kind of particle. The particles may be atoms or molecules. Water, gold, oxygen, salt, sugar, and snow flakes are all pure materials.

Two or more pure materials mixed together are called a **mixture.** Soil, ocean water, air, blood, and chocolate chip cookies are all mixtures.

There are two kinds of mixtures. In some mixtures, chunks of different pure materials are mixed together. You can usually see the bits of the different materials. Soil and chocolate chip cookies are this kind of mixture.

In the other kind of mixture, separate particles are mixed together. Air is a mixture of oxygen, nitrogen, and other gas molecules. Ocean water is a mixture of salt particles and water molecules. **Solutions** are formed when the particles of one material are scattered among the particles of a liquid.

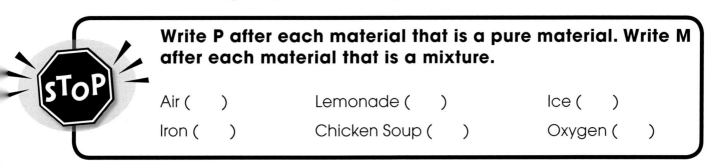

Write P after each material that is a pure material. Write M after each material that is a mixture.

Air (   )   Lemonade (   )   Ice (   )

Iron (   )   Chicken Soup (   )   Oxygen (   )

When salt is mixed with water, it seems to disappear. But the salt is in the water, and it is still salt. We can't see it because it is separated into single particles. When we make this kind of mixture we say the solid **dissolves** in the water. The amount of solid that will dissolve is called its **solubility.** Dissolving is a physical change and solubility is a physical property.

Mixtures can usually be separated into their parts. When heat is added to salt water, the water **evaporates,** and the solid salt is left behind. A mixture of salt, sand, and sawdust can be separated by adding water. The sand sinks, the sawdust floats, and the salt dissolves in the water.

Mixtures and Solutions

1. Put a check mark (✓) next to the answer that is most correct.

a) Which material is a mixture?

- ○ **A** table salt
- ○ **B** lemonade
- ○ **C** aluminum
- ○ **D** snow flakes

b) Which is a pure material and not a mixture?

- ○ **A** blood
- ○ **B** ice
- ○ **C** milk
- ○ **D** soil

c) Which property could be used to separate sand and sugar?

- ○ **A** color
- ○ **B** hardness
- ○ **C** size
- ○ **D** solubility

2. Salt, sand, and sawdust can be **separated** in four steps. Number the steps from **1** to **4** in the order they should be done.

○ **a)** Remove the sawdust from the top.

○ **b)** Evaporate all the water to get the salt.

○ **c)** Pour the water off of the sand.

○ **d)** Dump the mixture into a bucket of water.

NAME: _____

Mixtures and Solutions

3. What is a mixture?

_____

_____

4. What does solubility mean?

_____

_____

Extensions & Applications

5. Separating a Mixture

Suppose you have a mixture of sand, marbles, sawdust, and blocks of wood. You can separate these four things with a window screen, a bucket, and water. This will take three steps.

The screen is used in the first step.

The bucket and water is used in the second and third steps.

a) Describe the three steps.

Step One

_____

_____

Step Two

_____

_____

Step Three

_____

_____

b) Which properties of the materials made it possible to separate the mixture?

_____

_____

Finding Changes In the Kitchen

A picture of a kitchen and kitchen appliances is shown below

Physical Change: Blender chops things into smaller pieces.

Toaster oven

Blender

Range top

Microwave

Sink

Coffee Maker

Many physical and chemical changes take place in the kitchen.

One physical change is shown by the box and arrow.

1. Look at the picture carefully. How many places you can find in the kitchen where physical and chemical changes can happen? You may want to read some things about the science of cooking to help you understand the changes better.

2. Make more boxes and arrows like the one above to show where the changes you found take place.

3. In the boxes, tell whether each change is a **chemical change** or a **physical change.**

4. Tell the **cause** of as many changes as you can. For example, many changes in a kitchen are caused by adding or removing heat.

5. If you think you will need more room, copy the picture of the kitchen and paste it onto a larger piece of paper. You may also use a picture like it cut from a magazine or found on the Internet.

Chemical Changes and Conservation of Mass

CONSERVATION OF MASS is one of the laws of science. "Conserved" means something stays the same. So this law says that no mass is lost or gained during a chemical change. This is also true of physical changes. You can do experiments to show that this is true.

Experiment 1

For the first experiment you will need a piece of fresh bread, a tablespoon of water and a container. You must be able to see through the container and be able to seal it very tightly. You will also need a scale or balance that can tell very small differences in weight. Ask your teacher if there is an "analytical balance" in your school. Ask if someone could weigh some things on for you.

Steps:

1. Put the bread and water in the container and seal it tightly.
2. Weigh the container with the bread and water in it.
3. Put the container in a sunny window or other warm place.
4. Wait until the bread is covered with mold. (Getting moldy is a chemical reaction.)
5. Weigh the container again.

Experiment 2

For the second experiment you will need a few small iron nails or some iron filings. The nails should be plain iron and not coated with anything. Iron filings will work better.

Steps:

1. Weigh the iron nails or filings carefully.
2. Put the nails or filings outside in a place where they will get sunlight and where dew and rain can get on them.
3. Wait until the iron is covered with rust. (Remember rusting is a chemical reaction.)
4. Bring the nails or filings inside. When you are sure they are dry, weight them again.

A. **Did the weight change in the first experiment?**

B. **Did the weight change in the second experiment?**

C. **If the results were different in the two experiments, explain the difference.**

D. **Do you think mass was conserved in both experiments? Explain your answer.**

Separating a Mixture

One property we have not talked about is MAGNETIC property. This property can help separate some mixtures. Magnets attract and hold onto anything made of iron. Therefore, they can be used to separate things made of iron from other things. In this activity you will make a plan to separate a mixture of SIX things using tools from a list.

This mixture is really messy. In a bucket, all mixed together, are wooden toothpicks, sand, sawdust, sugar, copper pennies, and steel sewing needles. (Steel is kind of iron.)

These six materials can be **separated** using the bucket, water, a screen, a hot plate, a metal pot, and a magnet.

Tell how you would separate the materials. Describe each step. It is possible to separate them with just **five** steps. You may write the steps in a **list** or show them in a **flow chart**. The beginning of a flow chart is shown below.

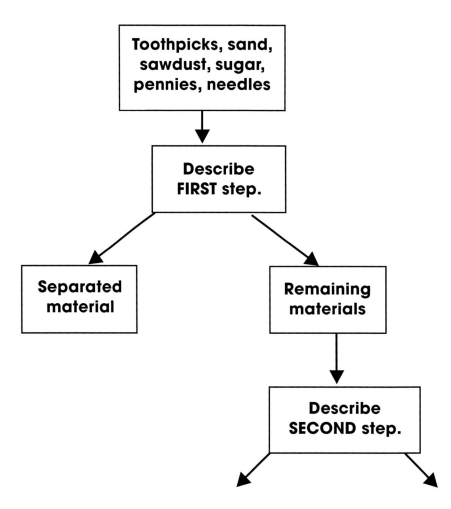

Photosynthesis, An Important Chemical Change

You learned earlier about an important chemical change that takes place in PLANTS. Plants turn carbon dioxide and water into oxygen and food molecules. Our bodies get energy from the food molecules. Do you know where the plants get the energy they put in the food? All that energy comes from the sun.

The scientific name for this reaction is **photosynthesis.** A material in plants called **chlorophyll** soaks up the sun's energy. The plant uses the energy from the sun in the photosynthesis reaction. Chlorophyll is green. It is what makes most plants green. Wherever you see green in a plant, photosynthesis can happen.

Experiment

For this experiment, you will need a small sheet of paper. It should be thick enough so that light cannot shine through it. You will also need something to cut the paper and some tape.

You are going to make a **pattern on a leaf.** To make the pattern, you will blocking some light from the leaf and let some light shine on the leaf. Where light hits the leaf it will be green.

Steps:

1. Cut holes in a piece of paper to make a word or picture that you want to see on the leaf. You could cut out the letters of your name; or, if you are very patient, the word "photosynthesis". Remember, whatever you cut out will have to fit on a leaf.

2. Find a large, strong leaf that gets sunlight. Tape the paper with the cut-out word or picture to the side of the leaf that gets the sun. Put it on so that the leaf is completely covered except for the cut-out.

3. Every few days, peek under the paper to see if the picture or word is starting to show up.

4. When you have a good picture, remove the leaf and bring it to school.

On the Internet, you can see pictures like this made by an artist by searching for "chlorophyll art"!

Crossword Puzzle!

Across

1. How much space something takes up
4. How much matter is in something
5. A material dissolved in a liquid
8. Something light cannot pass through
9. A particle that cannot be divided with everyday tools
11. A new material formed when something combines with oxygen
13. What iron does when it reacts with oxygen
16. Something that has mass and takes up space
17. The state of matter that has a fixed shape and a fixed volume
18. Some light passes through it and some does not

Down

2. See 16 Across
3. What water is doing at 212°C
4. What a solid does when you add heat
6. A material that is not in the gas state and not in the solid state
7. The change from gas to liquid
10. Two pure materials scrambled together
12. Either an atom or a molecule
14. Oxygen is one of these
15. It keeps you from floating off into space

NAME: _____

Word Search

Find all of the words in the Word Search. Words are written horizontally, vertically, diagonally, and some are even written backwards.

A	B	V	O	L	U	M	E	R	T	D	H	W	X	G	H
D	C	B	C	X	D	P	Q	R	S	F	J	M	Y	J	K
E	F	P	D	L	I	O	B	S	U	F	O	R	C	E	W
H	G	R	F	G	U	D	T	D	R	T	D	T	Z	Y	R
I	J	O	P	A	Q	U	E	G	A	I	X	S	M	P	E
L	K	P	R	H	I	T	V	A	S	W	E	I	G	H	T
S	M	E	S	O	L	I	D	S	Z	Z	A	R	M	Y	T
N	E	R	J	E	T	N	O	X	E	A	K	E	B	S	A
O	P	T	M	K	M	L	W	E	R	U	P	Q	C	I	M
R	Q	Y	T	I	V	A	R	G	B	A	L	P	D	C	X
S	T	X	Y	E	L	F	S	C	H	E	M	I	C	A	L
V	U	W	Z	A	L	M	X	S	C	G	M	N	F	L	Y

atom	gravity	physical
boil	liquid	property
chemical	matter	pure
dissolve	melt	rot
force	mixture	rust
freeze	opaque	shape
gas	oxide	solids
mass	volume	weight

Comprehension Quiz

Part A

Circle T if the statement is TRUE or F if it is FALSE.

T   F   1) Mass is a property of matter

T   F   2) Atoms and particles are two kinds of molecules.

T   F   3) When water boils, it changes into a new material.

T   F   4) You would have less weight on the moon than you do on Earth.

T   F   5) Smashing a pumpkin is a chemical change.

T   F   6) When salt dissolves in water, it forms a mixture.

T   F   7) Chemical changes cause atoms to fasten together a different way.

⑦

Part B

Put a check mark (✓) next to the answer that is most correct.

1) When water changes from a gas to a liquid it is called
- ○ **A** boiling
- ○ **B** condensation
- ○ **C** evaporation
- ○ **D** freezing

2) Which is a property of glass?
- ○ **A** It is soluble
- ○ **B** it is opaque
- ○ **C** it is flammable
- ○ **D** it is transparent

3) Which tool could be used to separate sugar from water?
- ○ **A** a screen
- ○ **B** a refrigerator
- ○ **C** a kitchen stove
- ○ **D** a bucket of water

③

SUBTOTAL: /10

Properties of Matter CC4504

Comprehension Quiz

Answer each question in complete sentences.

1. Describe the **motion** of particles in each state of matter.

○3

_____

_____

_____

2. Using the words "mass," "space," and "atoms," tell **three** things that are true of all matter.

○3

_____

_____

_____

3. What does the **density** of a material tell about the way particles are packed in a material? Name the **two** things you need to know to find the density of a material.

○3

_____

_____

_____

4. What is a **physical change**? Give an example of a physical change. What is a **chemical change**? Give an example of a chemical change.

○4

_____

_____

_____

5. Explain how a mixture of salt and water is different from a mixture of pebbles and water.

○3

_____

_____

_____

SUBTOTAL: /16

1.
a) F
b) T
c) F
d) F
e) T

2.

3. Particles of a solid can't change their positions.

4. The particles are slowing down.

5. Gas particles are far apart.

6. Answers will vary
(16)

A. condensation
B. removed **C.** slower
D. freezing **F.** slower
G. melting **H.** added
K. added **L.** faster
(17)

1.
a) L
b) G
c) S
d) L
e) S
f) G
g) S

2.
a) solid, liquid
b) liquid, gas
c) liquid, solid
(12)

a) freezing
b) condensing
c) melting
d) evaporating, boiling
e) melting
f) condensing
(15)

yes yes

no yes

no no
(13)

3. You would come to a piece that was just one atom.

4. No mass is lost in physical changes.

5. Accept any reasonable answer.
(10)

a) Democritus and Dalton
b) Aristotle
c) Aristotle
d) Dalton
e) Dalton
(11)

1.
a) B
b) B
c) C

2.
a) **Cross out:**
sound
a deep thought

b) **Circle:**
air
the planet Earth
an ant
an elephant

c) **Underline:**
air
the planet Earth
an ant
an elephant
(9)

1.
a) molecule
b) matter
c) atom
d) particle
e) mass

2.
a) yes
b) yes
c) no
d) yes
e) yes
(7)

Answers will vary
(8)

3. Accept one of: A new material is formed during a chemical change but not during a physical change. (OR) Atoms are connected in a different ways after a chemical change but not after a physical change.

4. Removing heat slows the particles down.

5.
A. No

B. Answers will vary

C. Water may have condensed on the cup, increasing the weight; or water may have evaporated, decreasing the weight

A. It collapsed

B. It stayed the same

C. It increased

D. The particles slowed down and moved closer together

(27)

1.
a) D

b) A

c) A

2.
a) Particle

b) gas

c) density

d) heat

e) motion/spacing

f) spacing/motion

(26)

1.
a) F
b) F
c) T
d) T
e) F

2.
Melting butter

Breaking a pretzel

Boiling water

Clothes drying on a line

(23)

The density of steam is less because the particles are farther apart.

(24)

3. Light does not pass through it.

4. Density tells how closely the particles are packed together.

5. Answers will vary

(22)

1.
a) opaque

b) density

c) melting point

d) weight

e) temperature

2.
a) F
b) F
c) T
d) T
e) F
f) F

(21)

1.
a) B

b) C

c) A

2.
a) texture

b) transparent

c) mass

d) volume

e) density

(18)

People do not have enough mass.

(19)

1.
a) P
b) C
c) C
d) P
e) C

2.
a) F
b) F
c) T
d) T
e) F

(28)

Possible answers: melt, break, bend the candle

(30)

1.
a) B
b) C
c) B

2.
a) chemical
b) water
c) atoms
d) physical

(31)

3. Atoms are connected in new ways to form new molecules.

4. Possible answers: color change, bubbles, volume change

5. Answers will vary

(32)

1.
a) T
b) T
c) F
d) F
e) F

2.
a) A
b) B
c) D

(33)

Possible answers:
Slowly – A type of corrosion
Quickly – A type of combustion
Explosively – Some explosive material

(35)

1.
a copper penny
dry firewood   (coal)
(gasoline)
an iron nail

2.
a) charcoal and oxygen
b) carbon dioxide and water
c) aluminum and oxygen
d) food molecules and oxygen
e) hydrogen and oxygen
f) oxygen and iron

(36)

3. Accept one of:
A change that forms a new material
OR
A change that causes atoms to be attached in a new way

4. Possible answer: Tells how or when a material will change to form a new material

5. Step 3: Carbon dioxide is in the balloon. Water is in the bottom of the bottle, and sodium acetate is dissolved in the water.

Step 4: The match went out because there was no oxygen in the bottle, only carbon dioxide.

(37)

1.
a) physical property

b) pure material

c) dissolve

d) solution

e) mixture

f) physical change

2.
a) **T**

b) **T**

c) **F**

d) **T**

e) **F**

(38)

M, M, P;
P, M, P (39)

1.
a) ⊘ B

b) ⊘ B

c) ⊘ D

2.
a) ②

b) ④

c) ③

d) ①

(40)

3.
Possible answer:
A combination of two or more pure materials

4.
Possible answer:
How much of a material will dissolve in a liquid

5.
Accept any reasonable answers

(41)

A. No

B. Yes

C. No matter could enter or leave in the first experiment. In the second experiment, no iron left, but oxygen from the air combined with the iron and added to the mass.

D. Yes, because the mass gained by the rusting iron equaled the mass lost by the air.

(43)

Answers will vary

(42)

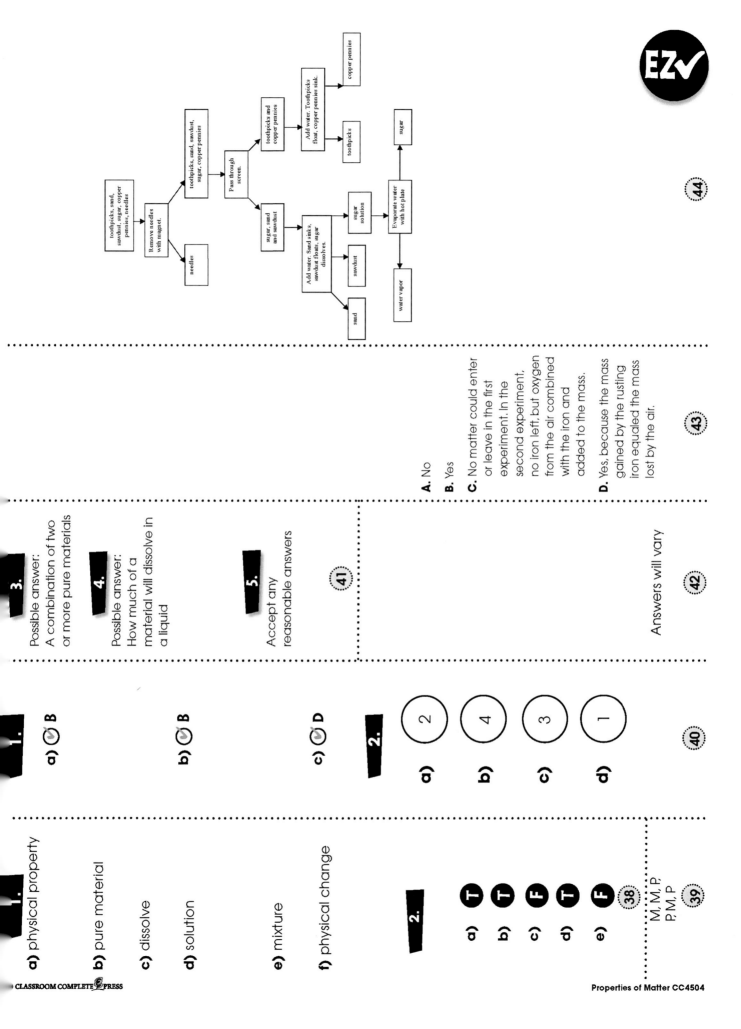

(44)

Across:

1. volume
4. mass
5. solution
8. opaque
9. atom
11. oxide
13. rusts
16. matter
17. solid
18. translucent

Down:

2. matter
3. boiling
4. melt
6. liquid
7. condensation
10. mixture
12. particle
14. gas
15. gravity

Word Search Answers

A	B	V	O	L	U	M	E	R	T	D	H	W	X	G	H
D	C	B	X	C	D	P	Q	R	S	F	J	Y	Y	J	K
E	F	P	D	L	I	O	B	S	U	F	O	R	C	E	W
H	G	R	F	G	U	D	T	D	R	T	T	T	Z	Y	R
I	J	O	P	A	Q	U	E	G	A	I	X	S	M	P	E
L	K	P	R	H	I	T	V	A	S	W	E	I	G	H	T
S	M	E	S	O	L	I	D	S	Z	Z	A	R	M	Y	T
N	E	R	J	E	T	N	O	X	E	K	E	R	B	S	A
O	P	T	M	K	M	L	W	E	R	U	P	B	C	I	M
R	Q	Y	I	V	A	R	G	B	A	L	P	D	C	O	X
S	T	X	Y	E	L	F	S	C	H	E	M	I	C	A	L
V	U	W	Z	A	L	M	X	S	C	G	M	N	F	L	Y

Part A

1) **T**
2) **F**
3) **F**
4) **T**
5) **F**
6) **T**
7) **T**

Part B

1) **B**
2) **D**
3) **C**

Part C

1. Particles in solids move slowest and stay in fixed positions. Particles in liquids move next fastest and can change positions. Particles in gases move fastest. (Answers will vary.)

2. All matter has mass, takes up space, and is made of atoms.

3. Tells how tightly/closely particles are packed in a material; need to know mass and volume to find density.

4. Physical – A change in physical properties that does not form a new material (or that does not change the way atoms are connected). Examples will vary.

Chemical – A change that forms a new material (or that changes the way atoms are arranged). Examples will vary.

5. Salt and water form a mixture of separate particles. Pebbles and water form a mixture of chunks of one material surrounded by another material. It is not evenly mixed. (Answers will vary.)

Properties of Matter CC4504

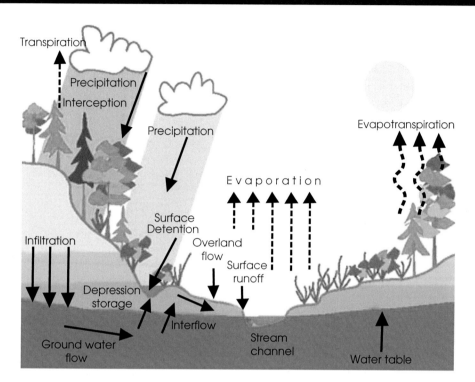

Evaporation as water leaves ocean, Condensation as water forms clouds, Freezing as water goes from clouds to snow, and Melting as water goes from snow-capped mountains to run off.

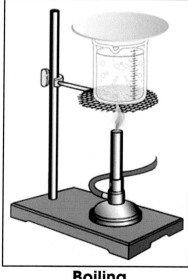

Boiling

Mass and Weight On the Earth and the Moon

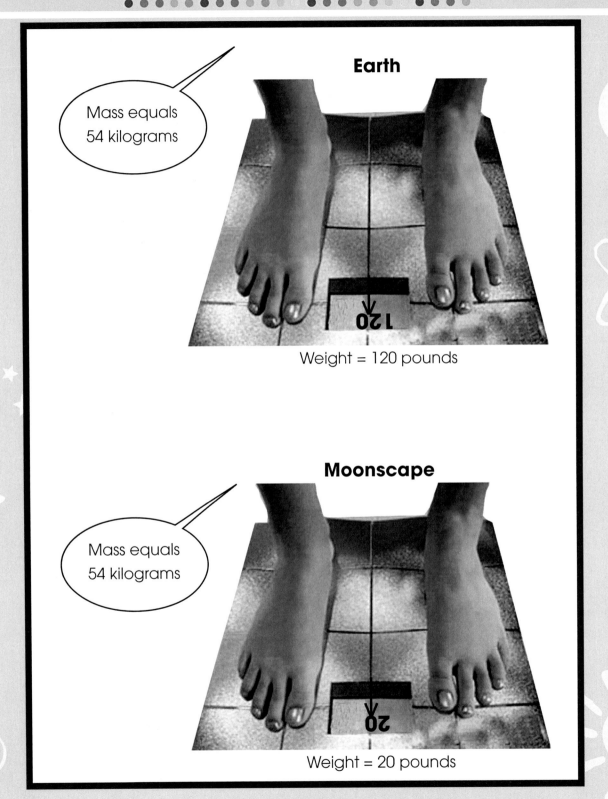

Earth

Mass equals 54 kilograms

Weight = 120 pounds

Moonscape

Mass equals 54 kilograms

Weight = 20 pounds

Chemical Changes and Physical Changes

Chemical: Forest fire burning

Physical: Water evaporating from oceans

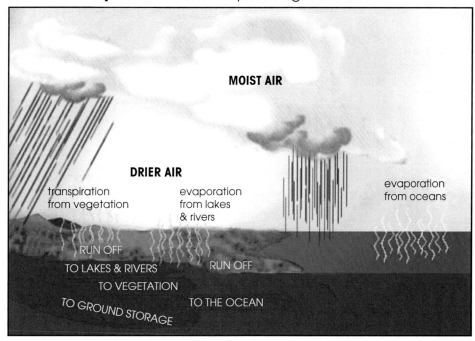

MOIST AIR

DRIER AIR

transpiration
from vegetation

evaporation
from lakes
& rivers

evaporation
from oceans

RUN OFF
TO LAKES & RIVERS   RUN OFF
TO VEGETATION
TO GROUND STORAGE   TO THE OCEAN

Finding Density

This is the **displaced liquid** method of finding density.

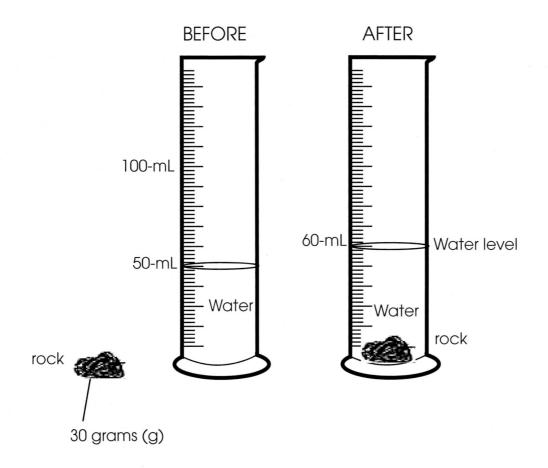

BEFORE   AFTER

100-mL

60-mL — Water level

50-mL

Water

Water

rock

rock — 30 grams (g)

Mass of rock = 30 grams.

Volume of rock = 60 milliliter (mL) – 50 mL = 10 mL.

Density of rock = 30 g/10 mL = 3.0 g/mL

Particles In Solids, Liquids and Gases

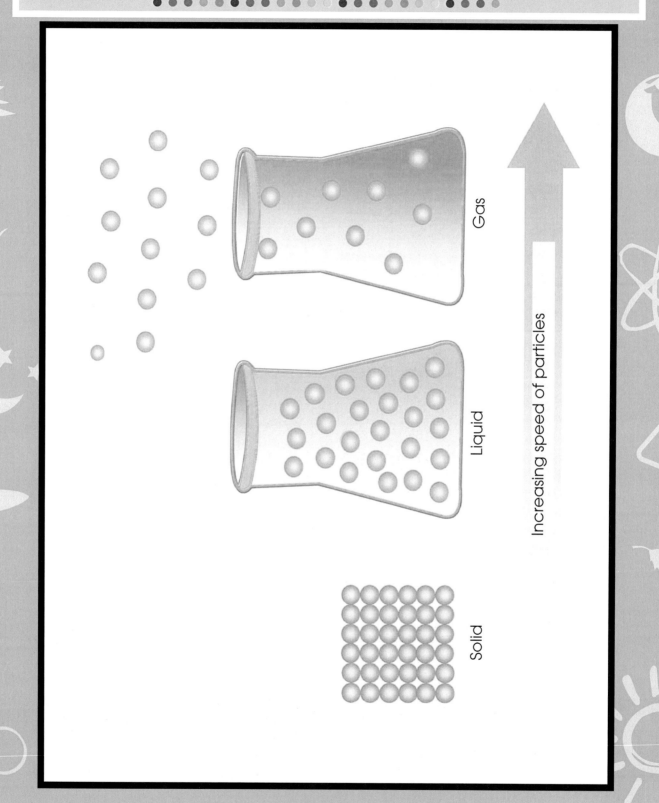

Gas

Liquid

Increasing speed of particles

Solid

Particles In Two Kinds of Mixtures

Sugar particles in solution

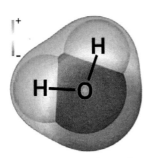

Water molecule

Sugar molecule

water particles

sugar particles

Sand grain

Sugar grain